NEW SONGS FOR CHILDREN

THE GINGERBREAD MAN BOOK

D0589154

WISE PUBLICATIONS
London/New York/Sydney/Cologne

Exclusive Distributors:
MUSIC SALES LIMITED
78 Newman Street, London W1P 3LA, England
MUSIC SALES PTY. LIMITED
27 Clarendon Street, Artarmon, Sydney, NSW 2064, Australia

This book © Copyright 1984 by
Wise Publications
UK ISBN 0.7119.0470.7.
UK Order No. AM 36013

Art direction by Howard Brown
Designed by John Gorham
Arranged and compiled by Frank Booth

Music Sales complete catalogue lists thousands of
titles and is free from your local music book shop,
or direct from Music Sales Limited.
Please send 25p in stamps for postage to
Music Sales Limited, 78 Newman Street, London W1P 3LA.

Printed in England at
The Camelot Press, Southampton.

SWEET GINGERBREAD MAN

Lyric: Alan & Marilyn Bergman Music: Michel Legrand

4

Fresh out o' the pan,___ Sweet Gin - ger - bread Man!___
All tas - ty and tan,___ Sweet Gin - ger - bread Man!___

C   G   Am7   B(sus4)   B   B(sus4)   B

Fresh out o' the pan,___ Sweet Gin - ger - bread Man!___

C   G   Am7   G   Am7   G

Twirl - in' a cane made o' pep - per - mint.   Uh, huh,   uh, huh.

G   Em   C   A7   D(sus4)   D

Nice ick - y, hand stick - y pep - per - mint!   Uh, huh,   uh,

G   Em   C   A7

D.C. al Coda

EL CONDOR PASA (If I Could)

Musical Arrangement by J. Milchberg and D. Robles
English Lyric by Paul Simon

way_____ Like a swan that's here and gone.
A man gets tied up to the ground, He gives the world its sad-dest
sound, its sad-dest sound._____ I'd
ra-ther be a for-est than a street. Yes I would. If I could,_____ I sure-ly

C   G

C   G

Em

G

would._____ I'd ra-ther feel the earth be-neath my feet. Yes I

would. If I on-ly could,_____ I sure-ly would._____

EARLY IN THE MORNING

Words & Music: Mike Leander and Eddie Seago

CHORUS

ear-ly in the morn - ing ov - er by the win-dow day is dawn-
ear-ly in the morn - ing ve - ry ve - ry ear - ly with-out warn-

Cm   Cm7   F7   Bb   Bbmaj7

ing when_ I feel the air I feel that life is ve - ry good to
ing I_ can feel a new-ly born vi - bra - tion sneak-ing up on

Ebmaj7   Am7   D7

me   you   know, In the sun there's so much yel-low some-thing in the
me   a - gain, There's a song bird on my pil-low I_ can see the

Gm   D7   G   Am7 G   Cm   Cm7   F7

To Coda ⊕

ear - ly morn-ing mea-dow tells_ me that to - day⎫ you're on your way and you'll_ be com-ing
fun in weep-ing wil-low, I_ can see the sun⎭

Bb   Bbmaj7   Ebmaj7   Am7   D7

ELUSIVE BUTTERFLY

Words & Music: Bob Lind

1. You might wake up some mornin', to the
Out on the new hor - i - zon, you may
2. You might have heard my foot - steps e - cho
You might have seen me run - ning through the

sound of some - thing mov - ing past your win - dow in the wind.
see the float - ing mo - tion of a dis - tant pair of wings.
soft - ly in the dis - tance, through the can - yons of your mind.
long, a - ban - doned, ru - ins of the dreams you left be - hind.

And if you're quick e - nough to rise, you'll catch the fleet - ing glimpse of
And if the sleep has left your ears, you might hear foot - steps run - ning
I might have e - ven called your name as I ran search - ing af - ter
If you re - mem - ber some - thing there that glid - ed past you fol - lowed

some - one's fad - ing sha - dow.
through an o - pen mea - dow.
some - thing to be - lieve in.
close by hea - vy breath - ing.

LITTLE BOXES

Words & Music: Malvina Reynolds

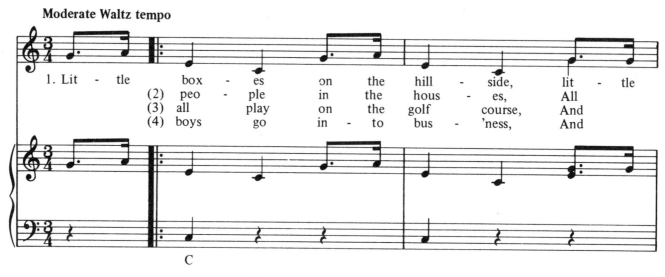

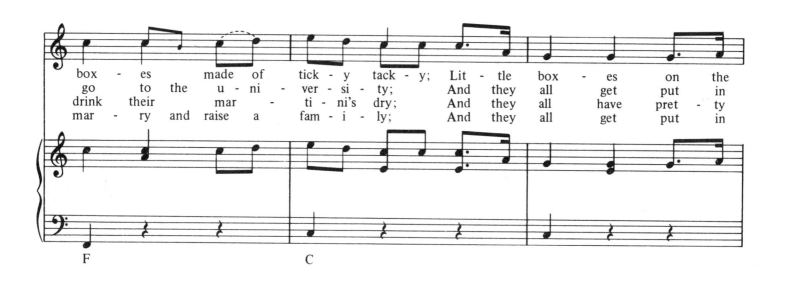

THE FIFTY-NINTH STREET BRIDGE SONG (Feelin' Groovy)

Words & Music: PAUL SIMON

DEAR OLD DONEGAL

Words & Music: Steve Graham

with me here and rich - es came ga - lore_____ And now that I'm go - in'
I - rish reel To greet the Yan - kee boy_____ We'll dance and sing the

Eb   C7   F7   Fm7 Bb7 Eb   Ab

back a - gain To dear old Er - in's isle_____ My friends will meet me
whole night long Such fun as nev - er seen_____ The lads - 'll be decked in

Cdim   Eb Bb7 Eb   Gm

on the pier And greet me with a smile_____ Their fa - ces sure, I've al -
cord - u - roy The col - leens wear - in' green_____ There'll be thou - sands there that I

Ab   Gm   F7   Fm Bb7   Eb

most for - got I've been so long a - way_____ But me mo - ther will in - tro -
nev - er saw I've been so long a - way_____ But me mo - ther will in - tro -

Eb7   Ab   Eb   Ab   Cdim

21

duce them all And this to me will say_____ Shake hands with your Un - cle
duce them all And this to me will say_____

Eb   C7   F7   Fm7 Bb7 Eb   Eb

Mike, me boy, And here is your sis - ter Kate_____ And there's the girl you

Ab   Eb   Ab

used to swing Down by the gar - den gate_____ Shake hands with all of the

Eb   F7   Bb7   Eb

neigh - bours_____ And kiss the col - leens all_____ You're as wel - come as the

Eb7   Ab   Eb   Ab   Cdim

SAILING

Words & Music: Gavin Sutherland

A LITTLE PEACE (Ein Bisschen Frieden)

Music: Ralph Siegel

Original German Lyric: Bernd Meinunger

English Lyric: Paul Greedus

27

for the world we live in. A lit-tle pa-tience and un-der-stand-

all the tears of sad-ness. A lit-tle hop-ing, a lit-tle pray-

ing for our to-mor-row a lit-tle peace. A lit-tle sun-

ing for our to-mor-

row a lit-tle peace.

rit.

a tempo

THE BARE NECESSITIES

Words & Music: Terry Gilkyson

Wher-ev-er I wan - der,_____ Wher-ev-er I roam,
When you__ pick a paw - paw or pric-kl-y pear,
(3) So just try to re - lax (Oh Yeah!) in my back yard,

F tacet_____* C7   F

I could-n't be fond - er_____ of my big home.
And you__ prick a raw paw_____ next time be - ware.
If you act like that bee acts_____ you're work-in' too hard.

tacet_____* C7   F

The bees are buzz-in' in the tree to make some
Don't pick the prick-ly pear by paw, when you pick a
Don't spend your time just look-in' a - round for some-thing you

F7   Bb   Bbm

hon - ey just for me.   You look un-der the
pear, try to use the claw.   But you don't need to
want that can't be found.   When you find out you can

F   G7   Dm7

WHEN I'M SIXTY FOUR

Words & Music: John Lennon and Paul McCartney

ONE OF THOSE SONGS (La Bal De Madame de Mortemouille)

English Lyric: Will Holt
Music: Gerard Calvi

one of those songs___ that start play-ing a-gain.___
sun com-ing up, or the rain com-ing down.___
all you re-mem-ber is "lah-dee-dah-dah."

___ Yes it's just one of those songs___ that you
Or else just the eve-ning you part-ed, you the
But lat-er on you'll re-call___ it in

hear for a while,___ that come in-to fash-
morn-ing you met,___ the love of your life___
some oth-er year,___ you may start to smile___

ion and go out of style.___ It's
you can nev-er for-get.___ The
or you may shed a tear.___ You'll

Gm7
C7
F
D7
Gm

36

one of those songs_____ that you think you for - got,_____
rea - son is sim - ple, the mem - 'ry be - longs_____
find that one part_____ of your life - time be - longs_____

but it's one of those songs_____ you can -
to one of those won - der - ful
to one of those won - der - ful

Bb   Bbm   F   D7

Gm7   C7

1.2.

not!   2. Be - cause it's
songs.   3. Well, this is

F   C7

3.

songs.

F

THIS OLE HOUSE

Words & Music: Stuart Hamblen

ONE DAY AT A TIME

Words & Music: Marijohn Wilkin & Kris Kristofferson

be   and   all   that   I   am.
low,   it's   worse now   than then.

Show me   the   stair - way,   I   have   to
Push - in'   and   shov - in',   crowd - ing my

C

G7   C   C7

climb;   Lord, for   my   sake,
mind,   So   for   my   sake,

F   C

teach me   to   take   one   day   at   a   time.
teach me   to   take   one   day   at   a   time.

G7   C   F

gone,_____ Sweet Je - sus,_____ and to - mor - row may

nev - er be mine._____ Lord, help me to -

day, show me the way one day at a time._____

time._____

FEED THE BIRDS

Words & Music: Richard M. Sherman & Robert B. Sherman

Though _____ her words are sim - ple _____ and few,

Lis - ten, ___ lis - ten, ___ she's call - ing to you:

"Feed _____ the birds, tup - pence ___ a bag,

Tup - pence, ___ tup - pence, ___ tup - pence ___ a bag."

A SONG OF JOY

Original Lyric: Orbe
English Lyric: Ross Parker
Music: Arranged by Waldo De Los Rios

stand a - lone with hands held out be - fore ____ him, Reach out and

C   G   D   G   D7   G   D7   G

take them in yours with love that en - dures for ev - er - more, Then ____

D   G   D7   G   B7   Em   C   D   G

— sing a song of joy for love and un - der - stand - ing

G7   C   G   D   G   D7   G

Come sing a song of joy, of

G   G   D7

freedom tell the sto - ry. Sing, sing a song of joy, for

G   D7   G   D7

man - kind in his glor - y, One might - y

Em   D   G   D7   G

voice that will bring a song that will ring for - ev - er - more Then

D7   G   D   G B7 Em C D G

sing a song of joy for love and un - der - stand - ing.

rall.

G7   C   G D7 G   D7   G

THE UGLY BUG BALL

Words & Music: Richard M. Sherman & Robert B. Sherman

NEVER SMILE AT A CROCODILE

Words: Jack Lawrence

Music: Frank Churchill

run, walk a-way, say, "Good-night!" not, "Good-day!"
rude, nev-er mock, throw a kiss, not a rock.
Clear the aisle and nev-er smile at Mis-ter

Bb   **F**   **Bb**   **F**   **Bb**   **F**

1 to Interlude   **2** *Fine*   Interlude

Cro - co - dile.   Cro - co - dile.   You may ver - y well be well - bred,

C7   **F**   **C7**   **F**   **Bb**   **F7**

Lots of e - ti - quette in your head, But there's al - ways

Bb   **F7**   **Bb**

D.C. al Fine

some spe-cial case, time or place, to for-get e - ti - quette. *Spoken* (F'r instance)

dim. poco a poco

F   **Bb**   **F**   **C7**   **F**   **(C7)**

BIBBIDI-BOBBIDI-BOO

Words: Jerry Livingston
Music: Mack David & Al Hoffman

THANK YOU FOR THE MUSIC

Words & Music: Benny Andersson & Bjorn Ulvaeus

I'D LIKE TO TEACH THE WORLD TO SING

Words & Music: Roger Cook, Roger Greenaway,
Billy Backer & Billy Davis

I'd like to build the world a home and fur-nish it with love

Grow ap-ple trees and hon-ey bees and snow-white tur-tle doves.

I'd like to teach the world to sing in per-fect har-mo-ny,

I'd like to hold it in my arms and keep it com-pa-ny.

D.%. al Fine

61

DO-RE-MI

Words: Oscar Hammerstein II
Music: Richard Rodgers

I WHISTLE A HAPPY TUNE

Words: Oscar Hammerstein II
Music: Richard Rodgers

when I fool the peo-ple I fear, I fool my-self as well! I

G   Gm   D7   G7

whis-tle a hap-py tune, And ev-'ry sing-le time, The

C   C7   F

hap-pi-ness in the tune con-vinc-es me that I'm not a-

G7   C   G7

fraid.   Make be-lieve you're brave and the

C   no chord   F

trick will take you far. You may be as brave as you

make be-lieve you are. *(Whistle)*

You may be as brave as you make be-

lieve you are.

CHIM CHIM CHER-EE

Words & Music: Richard M. Sherman & Robert B. Sherman

curled, 'Tween pave-ment and stars, is the chim-ney sweep world. When there's

G7   Gm7   Dm   E   A7

'ard-ly no day nor 'ard-ly no night, There's things 'alf in

Dm   F+   F   G7   Gm

sha-dow and 'alf-way in light, On the roof-tops of Lon-don, coo, what a

Dm   A7   Dm   Gm   Dm   A7 G A7

D.%. al Coda   ⊕ *CODA*

sight.   Chim chim-in-ey, Chim chim, cher-ee, chim cher-oo!

mf   *ritard.*

Dm   Gm   Dm   A7 G A7   Dm

69

SING

Words & Music: Joe Raposo

Sing! Sing a song. Make it simple to last your whole life long._____ Don't worry that it's not good e-nough for an-y-one else to hear. Sing! Sing a song!_____

MY FAVOURITE THINGS

Words: Oscar Hammerstein II
Music: Richard Rodgers

When the bee stings, When I'm feel - ing sad, ____

Am6   B7   Em   C

____ I sim - ply re - mem - ber my fa - vour - ite things and

A7

then I don't feel   so   bad. ____

G   C   G   Am7   D7   G

Am7   G   Am7   G no chord

SCARBOROUGH FAIR/CANTICLE

Arrangements and Original Counter Melody: Paul Simon and Art Garfunkel

BRIGHT EYES

Words & Music: Mike Batt

i - zon
trees_____

a strange glow in the
a cold sound in the

C   G

sky_____
air_____

a strange glow in the
a cold sound in the

a strange glow in the
a cold sound in the

and no - bo - dy seems_ to know
and no - bo - dy ev - er knows

C   G

D   D/C

where you go
when you go

and what does it mean
and where do you start

G   C

B/D#

CHORUS

oh   oh   is it a dream?
oh   oh   in - to the dark.

Bright_ eyes_

C#dim   G/D   D7   G

burn - ing___ like___ fire,___

Bright___ eyes___ how can you close___ and fail___

How can the light___ that burned___

___ so bright - ly sud - den - ly burn___ so pale?___ Bright eyes.__

STARMAKER

Words & Music: Carole Bayer Sager and Bruce Roberts

GRANDMA'S FEATHER BED

Words & Music: Jim Connor

said that I'd trade 'em all___ plus the gal down the road for Grand-ma's feath - er bed. I'd trade 'em all___ plus the gal down the road.... It was bed. We did-n't get much sleep, but we had a lot of fun on Grand-ma's feath - er bed.

D.%. al Coda

CODA

89

ANNIE'S SONG

Words & Music: John Denver

storm in the des - ert,_____ like a sleep - y blue

F   G   Am   F

o - cean,_____ you fill up my sens -

C   C/B   Am7   C/G   F

es,_____ come fill me a - gain._____

Em   Dm   G7   C   Csus4

Come, let me love you,_____ let me
sens - es_____ like a

C   F   G   Am